Bernard Bunting
and the Wet French Fries

Ro Willoughby

Illustrated by Tony Kenyon

By the same author:
Bernard Bunting: The Missing Birthday
Bernard Bunting: The Spider Spotter/The Worm Doctor

First published 2003
Cover design and illustration: Nick Ward

Scripture Union, 207–209 Queensway, Bletchley,
Milton Keynes, MK2 2EB, England.
Email: info@scriptureunion.org.uk
Website: www.scriptureunion.org.uk

ISBN 1 85999 636 1

British Library Cataloguing-in-Publication Data.
A catalogue record of this book is available from the British
Library.

Printed and bound in Great Britain by Creative Print and Design
(Wales) Ebbw Vale.

♭ Scripture Union is an international Christian charity working
with churches in more than 130 countries, providing resources
to bring the good news about Jesus Christ to children, young
people and families and to encourage them to develop spiritually
through the Bible and prayer.

As well as our network of volunteers, staff and associates who
run holidays, church-based events and school Christian groups,
we produce a wide range of publications and support those who
use our resources through training programmes.

Contents

Dedicated to the Trailblazers at Croxley Green
Baptist Church with thanks for all the great times we
have spent together!

Thanks to David Lowe, aged 11, for his wise advice
and to my friends, the Hodapp family.

Chapter One

Jonah gets wet

Bernard Bunting was fed up. His family was going on holiday tomorrow, to France. So this evening Mum was packing clothes in a rucksack and piling food into two plastic crates. Dad was counting tent pegs, checking the camping equipment and the oil in the car. His sister, Babs, was worrying about what clothes to take.

Everyone was busy and Bernard didn't know what to do.

He sat glumly on his bed, staring at the wall. He wasn't looking at anything in particular. In the corner was a box of his toys. A pile of books was next to it, books that wouldn't fit on to the bookshelf. His chair was next to that.

"That's funny," he muttered. "I haven't seen that book before."

He jumped off his bed and pulled out a small floppy book from the bottom of the pile. The rest of the books fell on top of each other.

Uncle Ivan gave me this book when he came back from America. That was ages ago and I've never read it.

Jonah Gets wet.

Bernard turned to the first page.

Now Jonah did not like this message. He did not like the people who lived in Nineveh. He certainly did not want to tell them that God loved them. Why should God love people who lived so far away and did such dreadful things, such as stealing and cheating and lying and worshipping other gods?

So Jonah did a dreadful thing himself. He decided that instead of obeying God by going east to Nineveh, he would go west. He went to the port and found a ship going west, all the way to Spain.

Bernard put the book down on his knees. He could understand how Jonah felt. He found it hard to talk about Jesus to his friends. It would be even worse to have to tell people he didn't like about God!

> Bernard, where are you?
> Can you help me?

It was Bernard's mum. They were packing up the car. They had to leave home at 4 o'clock in the morning to get to Portsmouth to catch the 7 o'clock ferry to France. By the time they had finished, the car was so full that Bernard wondered just where he would sit.

Mum turned to him. "It's time for bed, Bernard. We've an early start. Go and have a bath and I'll be up in a few minutes."

Bernard ran upstairs. He did not usually go to bed so willingly but if it was time for bed, then it was nearly time to go on holiday! Bernard loved going

9

on holiday although he didn't like sitting squashed in the back of the car with Babs. (You might remember this from *Bernard Bunting: The Spider Spotter!*) Big sisters are not always nice to their little brothers!

While the bath filled up, Bernard picked up *Jonah Gets Wet* from his bedroom floor. He took it into the bathroom and sat down to read it on the loo. But he hadn't even opened the first page when, somehow, the book jumped out of his hand. It wobbled on the edge of the bath (which was right next to the loo) and then…

Bernard shouted, plunged his hand into the water, but it was too hot!

Ouch! Mum!!!!!!!!!

His mum rushed upstairs into the bathroom. She fished the book out of the bath. Its pages were stuck together and grey. She squeezed the front and back covers together. Drops of water dripped into the bath.

"Jonah *has* got very wet," she said looking at the title. "Where did you get this from, Bernard?"

"Uncle Ivan gave it to me ages ago when he came back from America. I've never read it—" Just then Bernard had a new thought: "—and I want to take it on holiday."

Before the book had dropped in the bath, Bernard hadn't wanted to take it on holiday. But now it was wet, he really did want to. In fact, he wanted to so much that he thought that he might even begin to cry. He couldn't explain why.

"Oh Bernard, do you have to?"

Bernard wanted to sound determined. So he said, "Yes!"

"Are you sure?" (That's what mums say when they want you to do something different!)

So Bernard said, "Yes!" even more firmly.

Mum sighed. She wasn't going to argue with Bernard.

"But how are we going to get the book dry?"

This was going to be very difficult.

It was summer so the heating was not on! The book couldn't dry on a radiator.

It was evening so there was no time to dry it on the washing line in the garden.

It was made of paper so it couldn't be dried in the tumble dryer.

Babs and Dad came into the bathroom. Mum was frowning and dabbing the book with a towel.

"I know," said Babs, who always had lots of bright ideas. (Sometimes Bernard hated her bright ideas.) "Why don't we dry it with a hairdryer?"

Everyone (including Bernard) thought this was a brilliant idea. Dad and Bernard went downstairs. Dad opened the book out, then turned the hairdryer on to **1** and began blowing warm air on to the front cover.

Two minutes later, the front cover was almost dry, but the pages inside were still very wet.

Dad gave Bernard the dryer. "You have a go," he said. "Don't put the dryer on full strength!"

Two minutes later the back cover was dry, but the pages inside were still soggy.

Bernard was bored and wanted Dad to take over. This was going to take ages. But Dad was busy packing things away.

So Bernard did the second silly thing of the evening. He turned the hairdryer on full and held it as close as he could to the inside pages. Within seconds there was a dry patch on the page. And seconds later, Bernard could smell a funny burning smell. He dropped the book, which closed immediately, and switched off the hairdryer.

The burning smell disappeared. Bernard sighed. He was just going to have to be patient.

By the time Mum or Dad thought of him again (which was a lot later), Bernard had managed to dry most of the pages. They didn't look as clean as they had done before. And some of the words were smudged. And the pages were all bumpy when he closed the book. But at least most of the book was dry. And after all this hard work, he was even more sure that he wanted to take *Jonah Gets Wet* on holiday.

He fell asleep very quickly. It was going to be a short night!

What do you get when you cross an elephant with a goldfish?

Swimming trunks.

Chapter Two

Bernard gets sick

Bernard was very deeply asleep when Mum shook him awake. It was quarter past three in the morning. It was very dark outside.

"Get dressed quickly, Bernard. Check you've got everything you want for the journey, then come down for breakfast. Don't be long!"

It was cold so Bernard put on his sweatshirt and some socks. He had packed his bag the night before. His bear had been in bed with him, so Bernard put the bear at the top of the bag. Then he added *Jonah Gets Wet*. The book had been left out all night to dry a bit more. It was only just a little bit damp.

Breakfast was a very quick piece of

toast and a drink. Bernard wasn't hungry. They were ready to leave.

The Buntings were taking the fastcraft from Portsmouth to Cherbourg. This would take them nearly three hours. They would then have to drive for five hours south, down to the Loire Valley. Bernard had been told that the River Loire was one of the longest rivers in France. They were staying on a campsite by the side of the river near a place called Saumur.

"I will get so bored driving such a long way," Bernard had said when he first heard what a long journey it was.

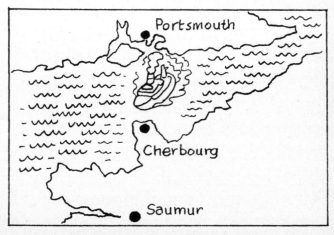

But the journey to Portsmouth was very quick. Bernard fell asleep again. This time when he woke up, it was light and they were nearly there.

Of course they had to join a queue of cars to show their tickets and passports. The woman in the office looked at the passports, peered inside the car to count four people and told Dad to join the queue in Lane 3. Driving on to the fastcraft was bumpy. Dad had to park the car so that it almost touched the bumper of the car in front. Their car was so close to the car beside them that Bernard had to hold his breath to get out of his door.

"You have got your backpack, Bernard, haven't you?" Mum asked. They were climbing the steps to the lounge above the car deck.

Babs spoke before Bernard could answer. "You've left it in the car, haven't you, Bernard!"

Dad sighed. "You find some seats," he said to Babs and Mum. "Come with me, Bernard. You're so thin that you can squeeze into our car to get your bag out."

All the cars were so tightly squashed together that it was difficult to see their car. At last Dad saw it.

"I am so excited about this holiday," Bernard told Dad as they climbed the stairs again. "Will it be very different in France?" (Bernard had never been abroad before.)

Dad nodded and grinned at Bernard. "I'm looking forward to this holiday too. Now, I wonder if it will be harder to find Mum and Babs than it was to find the car!"

All the seats were close together in rows, with three or four seats to a row. People were moving around. It was Bernard who spotted Babs' bag sticking out into the aisle. Mum and Babs had found four seats together. They were not sitting anywhere near a window.

This is Captain Roland speaking. I'd like to welcome you aboard. There is a strong wind out in the English Channel but we should get to Cherbourg in good time.

"What does that mean? A strong wind?" Bernard asked.

"It might get a bit bumpy," Dad said.

Bernard was hungry. Breakfast was a long time ago.

"Can I have something to eat?" he asked his mum.

"Don't eat much," Mum said, "but you could have a biscuit and a drink."

Bernard had got a lunchbox tube of chocolate biscuits in his bag. He pulled out three and ate them all quickly while no one was looking. He gulped down half of the bottle of apple juice that Mum had given him. He felt all excited and nervous inside!

Bernard had never been on a boat like

this before so once the journey had started, he went to explore. But there wasn't much to see. After ten minutes, he sat down again and got out *Jonah Gets Wet*. After all, Jonah got on a boat going to Spain and Spain was next to France. He read on.

Jonah was given a bunk to sleep on, right down in the bottom of the ship. He lay down and sighed with relief. He thought he had got away from God.

But a few hours later, he began talking to God. Perhaps it wasn't possible to get away from God after all. You see, the ship had run into a storm… but not just an ordinary storm with the odd flash of lightning and a bit of rain. In this storm, the

wind was so loud and strong that no one could hear themselves talk. In this storm, the waves hit the side of the ship with a great crash and this made the ship roll around and up and down. This storm lasted hour after hour. Would it never end?

Oh God, I feel so scared and so sick. Help me!

The fastcraft rumbled its way across the sea. It shook quite a bit, rocking from side to side. Portsmouth was far away. Bernard went to look through the window a couple of times but all he saw was grey, swirling sea. And the more that Bernard thought about Jonah, the more he began to feel a bit odd inside. It was the biscuits and the apple juice. In fact...

This is Captain Roland speaking again. The sea is quite rough. If you feel sick, please use the paper bag in the pocket in front of you and dispose of it in the toilets.

Some minutes later, Mum sat Bernard down next to her. He looked very pale and felt wobbly.

"See if you can get some more sleep," Mum said, putting her arm around Bernard.

Bernard was only too glad to close his eyes.

"Help me, God," he muttered to himself before he fell asleep again.

What did the sea say to the shore?

Nothing. It just waved.

Dear Reader, you didn't really want to read how Bernard was sick, did you? You can imagine what happened!

Chapter Three

Bernard gets wet!

The campsite was right by the side of the River Loire (you say this 'loo-ah'). But there was a fence between the tents and the river. Bernard helped put up the tent and laid the table for the evening meal. He was very hungry and tired!

He climbed into his sleeping bag long before it was dark.

"Don't wake me up when you come to bed," he ordered Babs. They were sharing a sleeping compartment. He knew she was likely to roll on top of him when she wriggled into her bag. Sisters are like that!

But the next thing he knew, the sun was shining through the canvas. He could hear sounds of breakfast outside!

He kicked Babs as he climbed over her to get out. But she didn't move!

"We're going to see a château," (you say this 'sha-toh') Dad announced as they ate breakfast, some time later.

"What's a château?" Bernard asked.

Babs looked at him in a superior way. "Don't you know what a château is, Bernard?"

"It's the French word for a castle," Dad continued. "There are dozens of them along the River Loire. When France had a king, over 200 years ago, dukes and counts and rich people built beautiful houses around here. Most of them were not like the castles we have in England. Our castles were usually built for fighting, to keep the enemy away. These castles were very grand palaces for living in. The owner invited grand people to stay. The bigger and grander the better!"

But castles are boring!

But this is one of the most famous and beautiful.

It took them over an hour to drive there. Once they were standing in front of the château, Bernard had to admit, it was very beautiful and very grand.

Chenonceau (you say this 'shhh-non-so'!) was a château built across the river – not the Loire but the River Cher (you say this share). It had five arches like a bridge, with long rooms built on top of

27

the arches. And it had beautiful gardens laid out in a pattern with hedges and pathways.

"Dad, can we hire a rowing boat and go under the arches?"

It was possible to hire a rowing boat for half-an-hour, to look at the château from the river. For a long time Bernard had had a secret dream in which he rowed a boat all alone across a great lake. But he had never been allowed to row a boat. Perhaps this was his first chance to have a go. It looked so easy.

"We'll see if there's time when we have seen inside the château," Dad said.

There were lots of stairs, and rooms with walls covered by carpets.

"What are all these carpets for?" Bernard asked in a loud voice.

"These are tapestries, Bernard, not carpets," Babs told him in a loud whisper. "They were to help keep the room warm."

Bernard particularly liked a dark room at the top of the château. Henry III, King of France, had been murdered in 1589. His wife, Louise, had gone to live at Chenonceau. She always wore white and had lived in this room for eleven years. It had a black ceiling. Bernard thought how miserable she must have been to stay inside such a gloomy room for so long.

Once outside, Bernard asked, "Can we go on a rowing boat now, Dad?"

"Come on then," Dad said. "Do you want to come, Babs?"

"No!" she replied. "I might get wet."

Dad sat in the boat with his back to the way they were going. The man who owned the boat pushed it away from the side. Dad held both oars tightly, one in each hand. He rowed slowly towards the arches. The river wasn't flowing very fast. Bernard sat still, waiting for his chance to row. Perhaps when Dad turned round, he would let Bernard row all the way back. They sat in silence.

"Can I have my turn now?" Bernard said after a few minutes.

Before Dad could answer, Bernard stood up and leaned over to reach for one of the oars. But…

It was cold in the water. And Bernard was very shocked. Down, down, down he sank. As he came up again, he heard Dad shout, "Grab hold of this oar, Bernard!"

Bernard held on tight as Dad pulled him towards the boat. Dad dragged him over the edge of the boat, then took off his jacket and wrapped it around his son. Bernard's clothes were sticking to him, like sticky tape. His trainers were so heavy. They were full of water. He pulled them off and emptied water into the river.

"What happened, Dad? Why did I fall in?" Bernard muttered miserably.

"You stood up too quickly. Rowing boats are very wobbly. You have to be careful. And rowing a boat is much more difficult than it looks. Look at that boat over there, going round in circles. The man doesn't know how to use the oars." Dad paused. "Next time you want to try to row a boat, we'll find somewhere a bit safer. Now let's get back!"

That evening Bernard read a bit more of *Jonah gets wet*. He had dried out, like the book, but it would take at least a day for his trainers to dry. They were stuffed with newspaper outside the tent flap.

The storm went on and on. Jonah began to think that the storm had happened because he had disobeyed God.

"You had better throw me into the sea," he told the sailors. "Then you will live, even if I drown. God will stop the storm once I am gone."

So the sailors did as Jonah said. They threw him overboard.

Jonah sank into the sea. Down, down, down he sank. The water was very cold. Jonah felt very shocked. As he came up again, he saw the ship sailing away. The great waves had got smaller. The sea was calm. The wind had stopped and Jonah could see a ray of the sun bursting out from behind a cloud.

"What am I going to do?" Jonah said to himself. "Where is the nearest land? And could I swim there, even if I knew where it was?"

I know how Jonah felt when he fell in the water, Bernard thought to himself. At least Dad was there to get me out!

Babs interrupted him. "Fancy getting wet again in the swimming pool, Bernard? You'll have dry clothes to change into this time!"

Bernard jumped up. "Wait for me!" he shouted.

Mum and Dad were sitting outside the tent, drinking coffee. As he walked past them, he whispered in Dad's ear, "Thanks for getting me out of the water!"

Dad grinned. "I'll teach you to row as soon as you're old enough!"

Why has a giraffe got a long neck?

Because it has smelly feet!
(It's a good thing it's not a centipede!)

Chapter Four

Bernard gets lost

Saumur, the town near the campsite, was
an interesting place. It had its own
château, on a hill, high above the town.
Years ago, there was only one old,
narrow bridge that crossed the River
Loire. But now there was a long road
bridge further down the river. You
could see it from the town. Saumur also
used to be famous for training horses for
use in the army. But there wasn't the
need for many horses like that these
days.

The next morning Bernard's family
explored the town. Bernard's trainers
were still soggy. They were old and
were really too small. Bernard's feet
had grown!

They walked into a wide space in the centre of the town. It was not exactly a square... more like a triangle. In the middle was a tall, willowy tree and around it were tables and chairs for people who had bought something to eat or drink from the three cafés nearby. There were several shops around the sides of the triangle... including a sports shop.

Babs and Mum said, "Let's look at this clothes shop."

Dad said, "I want an ice cream. Shall I get some for all of us?"

Bernard said, "I want to see if there are any trainers in the sports shop."

"Meet here in ten minutes," Dad said, pointing to a café that sold ice cream. "I'll have four ice creams with me and if they start melting, I'll eat them all!"

Bernard went to look in the sports shop window.

"I'll just pop inside," he said to himself.

 (...he wanted a new one for school)

  (...there were at least two that he liked)

 (...he wanted to try some on but didn't know how to ask in French and anyway, he didn't have any money with him).

He wasn't wearing his watch so he didn't know when ten minutes had passed. After what he thought was ten minutes, he wandered out into the triangle. Which café had Dad said to meet at?

He couldn't see Babs, Mum or Dad. Didn't Mum and Babs go into this clothes shop? Bernard peered inside. But the shop was empty.

Was it this café that sold ice cream?

Or was it this one?

The cafés all looked much the same. Bernard walked along all three sides of the triangle. His family had gone. Where were they?

One of the roads out of the triangle led to the river. Bernard knew that because that was the way they had come. He looked down this road. He could see the long road bridge in the distance. Could they have gone down to the riverside to eat their ice creams?

"My ice cream will have melted," Bernard muttered to himself.

He looked left and then he looked right. Where were they? And then he noticed that the tall, willowy tree in the middle of the triangle had gone. Where had it gone? Trees don't just disappear! It takes more than ten minutes to cut down a tree! The sports shop had gone too!

Suddenly Bernard had a scary thought. HE WAS LOST! It wasn't the tree or the sports shop that had gone. It was Bernard Bunting who had gone missing! He must have gone the wrong

way when he came out of the sports
shop.

Bernard sat down at a table outside
one of the cafés.

He sat very still and began to count to
1,000. He didn't have his watch on so
he didn't know how long he sat there.

"Help me, God," he said in his head.
"I really am lost and don't know what
to do."

He started counting to 1,000 again. All the time he was looking around for Mum or Dad or even Babs.

After a few minutes, the waiter at the café came up to Bernard and spoke to him. Bernard didn't understand. He just shook his head, feeling silly.

The man tried again. "Are you English?" he asked, in English this time.

Bernard nodded.

"Are you on your own?" he said, in English.

Bernard nodded.

"Are you lost?" he asked.

Bernard could feel tears beginning to grow in his eyes. He swallowed hard. Then the tears began to spill down his cheeks. The waiter pulled a big white handkerchief out of the pocket in his apron. He gave it to Bernard.

"I will get you a drink," the waiter said. "Sit here near the door. I can see you there. Your family will come soon."

He brought Bernard a big glass of orange juice. Bernard wiped his eyes.

Slowly he sipped his drink. He tried to remember the name of the campsite. But he couldn't. Could he get back to England on his own?

I'm all on my own.

"There you are, Bernard!"

It was Babs! Bernard had never been so pleased to see her. Dad and Mum were just behind her. Bernard jumped off his seat and ran to Mum. He burst into tears.

"It's OK, Bernard," she said. "You must have gone the wrong way when you came out of the shop."

They all made a fuss of him. Even the waiter made a fuss of him. He gave Bernard an ice cream, a double red strawberry one. Then they all went to the sports shop. They bought Bernard a pair of trainers that he really liked. He almost forgot his adventure.

That evening, he read a bit more of *Jonah gets wet*. Jonah was in big trouble. Much bigger trouble than Bernard had been in when he got lost. Jonah hadn't drowned. He hadn't swum to land. No one had come to rescue him. Instead, a giant fish had swallowed him! And now he was inside its stomach. Ugh!

God heard Jonah. Soon after Jonah had prayed, the fish had dreadful stomach ache. And he was sick, as sick as a dog… or a fish! Jonah was spurted out of the fish and on to the beach.

"God heard Jonah," Bernard told his dad.

"And he heard me too," Dad said. "I asked God to help me find you this morning."

"And I asked God to help me too," Bernard added.

What do you call a donkey with three legs?

A wonkey!

Chapter Five

Bernard's questions!

Bernard's mother always found exciting
things for the family to do on holiday.
This holiday they visited a zoo and a
mushroom farm (which was inside some
caves) and went on a boat and a train.
They even visited the château where the
Sleeping Beauty was supposed to have
lived. Bernard climbed up and up, right
up to the top of a round tower. Here,

inside a tiny room,
was a model of the
wicked fairy and her
spinning wheel. In
another room in the
tower he saw the
Sleeping Beauty
lying fast asleep.

Towards the end of the holiday, Bernard and his mum went shopping in the biggest supermarket Bernard had ever been in! And he had never been in a supermarket that had crabs moving around in a pool of water waiting to be bought… and then cooked!

"Mum, how long does it take for a crab to die once it is out of water?" Bernard didn't wait for the answer. (His mother didn't know, anyway!) "Could we try a crab, Mum? How do you cook them?"

Bernard's mum screwed up her nose. She knew that cooking a crab on a campsite is not easy.

"We're going out for a meal on the last night," she answered. "Why don't you order crab then?"

Bernard must have got up that morning with a question mark tied to his tongue! He asked so many questions that his mum and dad got fed up trying to answer them. He asked these four questions just while they queued up to pay for their food in the supermarket.

Why is this shop so big?

What's the French for 'sausages'?

Do I look French?

Are there lots of people called Bernard in France?

Mum put the food that they had paid for back in the trolley. She said, "Bernard, why don't you make a list of five things that the French do differently and five things that are the same as what we do in England?"

So back in the car, this is what Bernard wrote. His writing was a bit wobbly because the car jogged him and Babs knocked his arm twice.

The English and the French
1. Drive fast
2. Drink coffee
3. Go camping
4. Read newspapers
5. Have long motorways (but the French ones are not busy and you sometimes have to pay to use them!)
The French
1. Drive on the right of the road
2. Speak French
3. Eat long bread for breakfast
4.
5.

Bernard was just thinking what to put for numbers 4 and 5 when the car coughed, jerked and spluttered. Mum, who was driving, pulled the car to the side of the road and switched off the engine. She and Dad got out to see what was the matter.

(Mum spoke a bit of French but not a lot.)

Dad spoke to the children. "Mum's going to find someone to help. Why don't you two explore around here?

It's very quiet. Stay together and be back in half-an-hour. Have you got your watch on, Babs?"

Babs and Bernard scrambled out of the car. They had never been allowed to wander round on their own in France. This was an adventure!

"Let's find a sweet shop," Babs said. "I've got some money with me."

They walked down a long, straight road and then crossed over to the other side, being extra careful. In front of them was a large, dark building. It was a church, with an arch over the main door.

"Let's go inside," Bernard said. His legs were tired. He wanted to sit down.

But the church doors were locked. Bernard and Babs walked on down the road. It was full of houses. No sign of shops or even a park.

"We'd better get back," Babs said. "It's not really very interesting round here."

"Sorry we didn't get any sweets," Babs said as they reached the parked car. "We'll get some later today."

Dad was talking with a car mechanic. (The man spoke English.) Before long, a truck turned up. It towed the car to a garage that was close to the centre of the town. It would take two hours for the car to be fixed.

"Let's find a café and have a drink," Mum suggested. "We can sit outside."

"This will be better than sweets," Bernard whispered to Babs.

(A strawberry diabolo is a really good strawberry drink.)

Bernard asked plenty more questions while they waited.

Why did the car break down?

Some dirt got in the petrol tank. That made it cough.

> How did you get the man to come and help, Mum?

> I asked a woman where the nearest garage was. It was just round the corner.

> We tried to get into a church but it was locked. Are there lots of Christians in France, Mum?

"I think there are probably more Christians in Britain than in France. But when we get home we can find out what some Christians in France are doing by visiting the Scripture Union in France website. Scripture Union in France is called 'Ligue pour la Lecture de la Bible'."

The family was back at the campsite, cooking pasta for the evening meal. The meal was nearly ready. Bernard slid inside his sleeping area in the tent. By accident, he knelt on *Jonah Gets Wet*, which was lying on top of his sleeping bag. The front cover got creased.

*To read what Bernard found out about Scripture Union in France, turn over to page 79.

Bernard had read the book all the way through several times by now. He knew what happened, after the big fish had been sick. God had spoken to Jonah once again and told him to go to Nineveh. This time Jonah did what he was told.

By teatime, Bernard had one more question, at the end of this day when he had noticed so many differences between England and France.

Dad, Jonah went to visit the people of Nineveh. They were very different from him. Did he know their language or did someone have to speak for him?

Dad frowned. "I don't know," he said. "But I do know that Jonah didn't like them or their customs or how they behaved. He didn't really want them to turn to God."

"It must have been very hard for him to understand the people of Nineveh," Bernard said. "Poor old Jonah!"

What do you call a red penguin?

Sunburnt!

Chapter Six

Bernard and
the wet French fries

It was the last day of the holiday.

"You can choose what you want to do today," Mum promised Babs and Bernard. "And we're going out for a special meal this evening."

I want to go shopping, Mum!

Oh no! Not shopping!

Babs really did want to look around the shops one more time! Bernard certainly didn't want to do that.

So Babs and Mum went into Saumur to shop. Bernard and Dad decided to hire some bikes and go for a ride in the countryside.

"I hope I don't get too tired!" Bernard said.

"I could say the same," Dad said. "You use your bike at home much more than I do, Bernard. I am much more likely to get tired!" That made Bernard smile!

The two of them cycled along the side of the river for a short way. But the road was very busy and Bernard wanted to talk with Dad. On such a busy road, they had to cycle in single file.

"Let's turn right, down this lane," Dad said.

After that, they could cycle together. They came to a long village with houses built into the white rock. Some houses had three sides, but inside the house, the wall at the back must have been all bumpy, because it was made of rock.

"How did you know that?" Bernard asked. He was often amazed at what his dad knew.

"Oh, I read it in a tourist book," Dad replied.

They puffed their way to the top of a hill on the other side of the village. Now they could look down on the village, they could see the back gardens of houses. Many of them had chickens or grew peas and tomatoes.

They set off down the hill on the other side. Bernard pushed his foot down on one of the pedals. Wheee! He raced down, ahead of his dad. He didn't have to pedal at all.

"I'm coming!" Dad called after him.

Bernard's wheels went round faster and faster… and faster. The warm air whizzed past his face. He was almost at the bottom of the hill when…

Dad was already off his bike and bending over Bernard by the time he opened his eyes.

"Are you OK, Bernard? Can you sit up?"

Bernard closed his eyes again and wiggled his hands and ankles. He didn't really hurt anywhere. He had landed on a grassy patch. He felt a bit shaken but otherwise felt OK. He rubbed the back of his head. Dad helped him stand up.

"Wow, that was lucky," Dad said, "especially as we weren't able to hire any cycle helmets."

But the bike was not so lucky. It had a flat tyre and the wheel was a bit twisted. It had landed in another hole in the road.

"We can't cycle any further, can we?" Bernard said.

Suddenly he felt very cross. He so wanted to spend this morning cycling with Dad. Now it was all spoilt. Nothing was fair! And how were they going to get back to the cycle shop with the twisted bike?

"Don't be grumpy, Bernard," Dad said. "We'll have to walk. It isn't too far. You push my bike and I'll carry yours."

But it seemed a long, long way to Bernard. After only a few minutes he felt tired and cross. He and Dad played several I-Spy games. They sang their best songs. They told each other their best jokes.★ A fast red car whizzed past them. But after that nothing else passed them on the road. Bernard wanted to sit down.

Just then they heard the sound of an engine coming up from behind. An old van clattered past them. The driver had a good look at them as he passed. The van stopped just a little way ahead. The driver got out and spoke in French to Dad. Dad was able to make him understand what the matter was. (It was pretty obvious!) And before Bernard could say anything, the driver lifted Dad's bike into the back of his van, then Bernard's, and then all three of them

★*One of Bernard's best jokes is at the end of each chapter of this book.*

squashed into the front! The van stopped outside the cycle shop.

Back at the campsite shop, Dad and Bernard bought themselves an ice cream.

"I'm still fed up," Bernard said. "I really wanted to go on the bike ride. But it all went wrong. It wasn't fair!"

"I think that your friend Jonah must have felt like you did," Dad said. "Can you find *Jonah Gets Wet*?"

The vine that sheltered Jonah from the hot sun dried up and died! He was angry about that too! Jonah got hotter and hotter.

But God said to him, "You're angry because the vine has shrivelled up. You cared about that vine. I care even more about the people who live in the city of Nineveh. And I am very happy that they want to obey me."

Fancy, God cares for people however bad they are and wherever they live! Jonah couldn't think what to say after that. He certainly stopped being cross!

"Things didn't go Jonah's way," Dad went on. "But God knew best. Things don't always work out as we would like. You might think the accident with the bike wasn't fair, but God cares for us whatever happens. And he knows best."

That evening, the family went to a restaurant by the side of the river. Bernard couldn't decide what to eat. He wanted to try crab. But he also wanted to try mussels or 'moules'. (That's the French word for mussels. You say it as 'mools'.) He had seen other people with large bowls piled high with long blue-black shells. They broke open the shells and ate the mussels inside. But would he *like* crab or mussels?

"Look, Bernard," Mum said, "I'm having mussels so you can try one of mine. Dad is having crab so you can try a bit of his. Choose something you know you'll like."

So Bernard chose a steak with *'pommes frites'* or French fries, and lemonade to drink.

Their meal was brought to them. Bernard ate his first forkful of French fries. He broke open one of Mum's mussels. It had a smell he had never smelt before. He didn't like the taste after all. As Bernard cut into his steak, the hand holding his knife slipped. It somehow knocked into his lemonade and…

The wet French fries lay in a pool of lemonade. And Bernard had hardly eaten any of them! He felt just as he had done that morning. It wasn't fair! Why did things have to go wrong? Chips (or French fries) were one of his favourite foods. Then he remembered what Dad had said about Jonah. God cares for us whatever happens. And he knows best.

He looked up at Dad. Dad grinned.

"I don't know how you managed to do that, Bernard. Let's see if they'll let you have some more French fries."

The second plate of chips was bigger than the first!

Why was 9 afraid of 7?

Because 7 ate 9.

Chapter Seven

Splash!

There was one week of the school holidays left once Bernard had got home from France. Mum was busy getting all the things Bernard and Babs needed for the start of the new year.

> We must get you a new pair of shoes, Bernard!

> How big is the crack in your lunchbox, Babs? We must get you a new one.

Bernard and his friend, Brian, walked to school on the first day of term. They had so much to talk about, although Brian wasn't really listening. He had been given a small, hard ball. He kept bouncing it on the pavement. Every now and then it bounced into the road.

"Be careful!" Bernard called out. "It'll bounce away."

The main entrance to school looked different. There was a fence down the side of the main path, with a gate in the middle. On the other side of the fence was a pond! Bernard's classroom was on the other side of the pond.

"We can have a good look at the pond," Brian said. "We can see it from the classroom window."

"I wonder what it's there for," said Bernard. "A home for frogs?"

That reminded him of how the French sometimes eat frogs. He began to tell Brian about going to France and eating French fries and falling off his bike and getting lost. And getting wet!

Mr Zimmer, the head teacher, told
the whole school all about the pond in
assembly.

"This pond has been dug so that we
can all find out more about pond-life.
The plants are very new so it will be
some time before we can use it. And
why do you think there is a fence
around it?"

Some of the smaller children put their hands up. Bernard and Brian sighed. It was obvious why the fence was there... to stop them going to have a look!

Mr Zimmer went on, smiling at the whole school. "It is to keep you safe. You can drown in a very small amount of water!"

At playtime, Brian and Bernard were the last to leave the classroom.

"Catch!" Brian called out to Bernard, throwing his ball to him.

Now, Bernard was not ready for the ball. He had been thinking about something else. He put out his hands to catch the ball but...

Brian was cross with Bernard. Bernard said that Brian should have thought before he threw the ball.

"We'll have to get it back," said Brian. "Come on!"

The two boys ran to the other side of the classroom and down the main path. Bernard looked around nervously. No one could see them. The staff room window was on another side of the school and the teachers on duty were in the playground.

The gate in the middle of the fence was locked! But a wooden tree trunk had been left at the end of the path next to the fence. It was just high enough to help someone over the fence.

"Quick, before anyone comes! You go, Bernard. It was you that missed it!"

Bernard wanted to disagree. But he knew they had so little time. He jumped on to the tree trunk and scrambled over the fence. He bent over to pick up the ball. As he did so, out of the corner of his eye he saw something in the pond move. He turned his head sharply, and too late…

The pond was brand new. It did not have much pond-life, but it had certainly got lots of mud. Bernard's foot was covered in mud and he was wet right up to his knee!

"Bernard!" Brian called.

But it was too late. Coming out of the main door was Mr Zimmer.

Mr Zimmer marched Bernard and Brian into his office. He was very cross with them. After Bernard's leg and foot had been cleaned he said, "You will both stand outside my office every playtime this week. I never expected you two boys to do something so silly."

Later in the day, the whole class talked about their holidays. Bernard was still feeling miserable. His leg was dry, but what would Mum say when she saw his wet shoe? It wasn't like the old trainers that had got wet when he fell out of the rowing boat. His school shoes were brand new.

"What did you do on holiday, Bernard?" Miss Phipps, his new teacher said, with a smile on her face. "You didn't get wet by accident, did you?"

Bernard screwed up his nose.

"Well, we went to France on the ferry," he started. And then he found he couldn't stop telling the class all about his holiday and how he had fallen into the river at Chenonceau.

And how he had spilt the lemonade over his French fries.

And he also told them about the book that fell into the bath by accident.

"And it was the book I wanted to take on holiday," he went on. "So we had to dry it with a hairdryer."

"But then I read it while I was away. It was about Jonah. God wanted Jonah to tell some people about God. But Jonah didn't like these people. So he ran away. And there was a storm. And Jonah was thrown in the sea and the storm stopped. But Jonah was swallowed up by a giant fish. The fish was sick after three days and…" Bernard carried on telling the story.

"At the end Jonah realised that God loves everyone wherever they live and even if we don't like them."

Everyone had listened while Bernard talked. It was very quiet when he finished.

"Thank you, Bernard," Miss Phipps said. "You must bring the book to school to show us."

Of course, Mum was cross that Bernard had disobeyed Mr Zimmer and had fallen in the pond. But when they got home, Bernard told Mum how the whole class had listened when he told them about the holiday and the story of Jonah.

Mum grinned at Bernard. "You were telling the whole class about God, weren't you? Was it very difficult to do?"

Bernard hadn't thought of that at all.

"Well, it wasn't hard," he said after a pause. "And they all listened. And Miss Phipps wants to see *Jonah Gets Wet.*" He thought for a bit. "I can tell the whole class more about God and Jonah!"

Bernard's last joke: What is green and white and hops?

A frog sandwich.

Scripture Union in France

Scripture Union helps children, young people and families in over 130 countries in the world. SU aims to help them to become followers of Jesus and learn to read the Bible. *Ligue pour la Lecture de la Bible* is the name of Scripture Union in France. In English this means, 'the organisation for reading the Bible'.

Ligue pour la Lecture de la Bible produces booklets to help people of all ages to read the Bible. For the children they produce *Le mini lecteur de la Bible* and *L'Explorateur.*

Followers of Jesus who live in other countries but speak French also use these books. These countries include Belgium, Switzerland, Canada and parts of Africa. *Ligue pour la Lecture de la Bible* also run camps for children as young as six and their families in the summer holidays. Some of these are tennis camps; others give opportunities for different outdoor activities and drama. SU also owns its

own campsite called Le Rimlishof. It is a beautiful centre in the mountains.

You can find out more by visiting their website: www.LLBfrance.com. If you don't speak French, you will need someone who does to help you!